Kirk *Cameron*   Ray *Comfort*

Present

The Way of the Master

How to share your faith
simply, effectively, biblically...
the way Jesus did

**FOUNDATION COURSE
STUDY GUIDE**

The Way of the Master Foundation Course
Study Guide

The Way of the Master Publications
P.O. Box 1172
Bellflower, CA 90706, USA
www.wayofthemaster.com

ISBN 1-878859-57-9

Edited by Lynn Copeland

Design and production by Genesis Group

Cover by Joe Potter (joepotter.com)

Printed in the United States of America

Contents

Getting Started

No doubt you have your fears and concerns when it comes to sharing your faith, but through this course you will discover a newfound courage. You will learn how to share your faith simply, effectively, biblically...the way Jesus did. This is accomplished by addressing the sinner's conscience, thus avoiding the intellect—the place of argument. That means you don't have to be an "expert" in anything. You will never again need to feel intimidated by intellectuals, atheists, or even the self-righteous. All you need is a desire to obey God...and a genuine concern for the lost.

The Way of the Master Foundation Course is designed as an eight-week study. Although it can be used by an individual, it is ideally suited for use in small groups. Evangelism can seem fearful and intimidating, and a group setting can provide the needed encouragement and accountability.

Each session includes a portion of a video, a discussion time, and a "homework" assignment. Each video segment is 28 minutes long; to allow adequate time for discussion, the recommended time for each weekly session is approximately an hour and a half.

Begin each lesson in prayer, asking God to give you a deeper understanding of His Word, particularly in the area of evangelism, and to give you a genuine concern for the lost.

Read the "Food for Thought"; perhaps one person can read it aloud while the others digest its content. Watch the video, then go through the discussion questions. Everyone should have a chance to weigh in on the answers. Thoroughly discuss each point, allowing different people to express their thoughts, but be careful to avoid arguments. Focus on the concepts presented, and keep the session moving forward. Take five to ten minutes for each question and then move on so you get through the material in the available time.

Lastly, go over the "Out of the Comfort Zone Activity," which is your weekly assignment. Be sure to complete this activity before you meet for the next session. This is the most important part of the course: we are to be doers of the Word, not hearers only. Each week you will be challenged to interact with others, sharing what you have learned with the lost in your community. This gentle, gradual process is designed to help you feel comfortable and confident as you share your faith. In the back of this study guide, you will also find additional material to help you move out of your comfort zone to reach the lost.

May God richly bless you as you take this often forgotten journey into the world of normal, biblical evangelism.

KIRK CAMERON
RAY COMFORT

Program 1: The Firefighter

Open in Prayer

Food for Thought

Thank you for caring about people and their eternal salvation. Two thousand years ago, Jesus said to His disciples that the laborers were few. They still are few in number, but by wanting to learn how you can reach the lost, you obviously want to change that. Pay careful attention to this first teaching, especially to the heartbreaking story of the firefighter. Be sure to make a judgment about what his punishment should be—and write it down as you watch the video. May God bless you as you begin this wonderful journey into *The Way of the Master*.

View the Video   The Firefighter

Discussion

1. How did you react as you heard the firefighter's story? Did you feel a sense of outrage? Why or why not? What did the firefighter do that was wrong?

2. Can you think of any justification for his lack of concern? Do you think the fire chief was justified in dishonorably discharging him from the fire department? What sentence did *you* give the firefighter?

3. What is the primary reason the Church exists on the earth? How will this differ from what it will be doing in heaven?

4. According to Bill Bright, what percentage of Christians actively share their faith with others? What do you think are the main reasons the vast majority don't share their faith?

5. Have you been playing the part of the firefighter, by failing to share your faith with those around you? How does that make you feel?

6. Who are the people whose salvation you are most concerned about? What are you doing about it?

7. How can prayer be a substitute for obedience?

8. With whom do you find it more difficult to share your faith: your family and friends, or complete strangers? Why?

9. Did you find it helpful to see someone on the program witnessing?

10. How would you describe your current attitude about the fate of those who are not born again: a) unconcerned; b) concerned; c) alarmed; d) horrified?

11. Do you feel well-equipped to share your faith?

12. What did you think of the conversation with the teenager at the end of the program?

Out of the Comfort Zone Activity

Call two Christians and say, "I'm taking an evangelism course, and as part of the homework I have to ask a friend a few questions. Can you help me with this?" Ask each person the following questions:

1. Do you share your faith regularly? Do you go out of your way to share your faith with strangers?

2. If not, why not?

3. What is the biggest reason you don't share your faith more often?

Write down their answers and bring them to the next session.

Close in Prayer

Program 2: The Mirror of the Ten Commandments

Opening Activity

Briefly share the results of the previous session's "Out of the Comfort Zone" assignment.

Food for Thought

The first step in learning to share our faith is to examine our own hearts. It is important to know our motivation for witnessing. The fuel that motivates us to share the gospel with others should be our gratitude to God for the cross, combined with a concern for the terrible fate of unbelievers. Who do you know who isn't saved and will one day be cast into the Lake of Fire? We should be horrified at the thought of this happening to *anyone*. If you're lacking the fuel of compassion for others and gratitude for your own salvation, the task of sharing your faith will become a chore, feeling loathsome and legalistic. If there's no fuel in your car, you'll have to push it instead of drive it. If you have to push the vehicle of evangelism, it will be a tiresome task, while driving it will be exhilarating. Without the fuel of gratitude, your attitude won't be an enthusiastic "I delight to do Your will," but a begrudging "I *have* to do Your will."

Each of us needs to have a Garden of Gethsemane experience, where we lay down our own will. It was in a garden where man first said, "Not Your will, but *mine* be done." And it's in a garden where we need to go back and say, "Not my will, but Yours be done." Don't be concerned that the rest of the church may be sleeping when it comes to seeking the lost. Just find a quiet place, get on your knees and say, "Father, the thought of sharing the gospel with strangers and my loved ones makes me sweat great drops of blood. Yet not my will, but Yours be done." Make it so real that the next time you're standing at Starbucks and you want to share your faith with the person standing next to you, you will remember your Gethsemane experience.

Before we continue, take two or three minutes right now for silent prayer, as you meditate on the cross and surrender yourself completely to the Lord.

View the Video **The Mirror of the Ten Commandments**

Discussion

1. Do you think the current fall-away rate of 80 to 90 percent has more to do with a lack of follow-up, or with the content of the message that led to the "decision"?

2. Why would an individual's understanding of his specific, personal violations of God's Law help the good news of the gospel to make more sense?

3. When witnessing to an unsaved person (whose sinful mind argues with God's Law), what is the place of common ground?

4. When sharing your faith, why should you try to move quickly from the area of the intellect into the area of the conscience?

5. According to Romans 3:19, what is one function of God's Law? Why is this function so important?

6. What do Romans 3:20 and Romans 7:7 say about God's Law?

7. According to 1 John 3:4, what is the biblical definition of sin?

8. Since we are saved only by grace, through faith, and not by the Law, what then is the purpose of God's Law for the sinner? (See Galatians 3:24.)

9. How effective do you think the Moral Law was in helping the young man on the video see his need for a Savior? Do you feel he was offended? Why or why not?

10. What was your reaction to the "Ten Beers and Ten Commandments" segment?

Out of the Comfort Zone Activity

1. Call two Christian friends (they can be the same people as in the previous session), and ask what they think is the purpose of the Ten Commandments.

2. Ask two other Christian friends to explain to you what they would say to nonbelievers about why they should become a Christian.

Write down their answers and bring them to the next session.

Close in Prayer

Program 3: The Motive of the Sinner

Open in Prayer

Opening Activity

Briefly share the results of the previous session's "Out of the Comfort Zone" assignment.

Food for Thought

We spoke previously about having a Garden of Gethsemane experience (surrendering your will to the Lord), and how it was in another garden (the Garden of Eden) that man said, "Not Your will, but mine be done." Just as there was a subtle serpent in that garden, so there will be a subtle serpent ever present in your Garden of Gethsemane experience. The Father of Lies has a weapon that will make you continually sweat drops of blood: it is the weapon of fear. So don't listen to his whispers. Every time you go to open your mouth for the Kingdom of God, you can be sure he will be there to say, "You can't do this." But when fear knocks on the door, send the Word of God to open it. Say, "I can do all things through Christ who strengthens me. The Lord is my helper; I will not fear."

The great key to conquering the fear of man is not to think of yourself, but to think of the person to whom you're about to speak. What is *your* worst-case scenario? It is simply "rejection." What is *his* worst-case scenario? *He* will spend eternity in the Lake of Fire. We don't have a choice—we must "warn every man." Therefore, let compassion swallow your fears, open your mouth boldly, and speak as you ought to speak (Ephesians 6:20).

View the Video The Motive of the Sinner

Discussion

1. Why do you think the Church turned away from the use of the Law and embraced the modern method of promising love, joy, peace, fulfillment, and lasting happiness?

2. Do you think sinners can be happy without Christ? (See Jeremiah 12:1.)

3. Explain what the word "righteousness" means to you.

4. Explain why it's not right to use the promise of peace and joy as drawing cards for salvation.

5. What was your motive for coming to Christ?

6. Explain why a sinner's *motive* for coming to Christ determines whether or not he will fall away.

7. What did you think of the singing man with the "Jesus" sign dancing in Hollywood?

8. What should we be telling the world about Jesus?

Out of the Comfort Zone Activity

Make the effort this week to greet at least two complete strangers each day until the next session. At the grocery store, the gas station, school, or work, practice being friendly with people you don't know. Learn to say to a complete stranger, "Hi. How are you doing?" This really isn't difficult and will bring unexpected smiles to people's faces. So go out of your way to greet someone, then note the person's reaction. This may sound overly simplistic, but it's a very important step toward sharing your faith.

Close in Prayer

Program 4: The Summary of Salvation

Opening Activity

Briefly share the results of the previous session's "Out of the Comfort Zone" assignment.

Food for Thought

In the popular movie *Raiders of the Lost Ark*, it seems that the filmmakers valued the golden ark rather than what it contained. The ark held God's Law, the Ten Commandments; the ark was merely the extravagant golden wrapper for the valuable contents. God *loves* His Law. It's a revelation of His moral character. Its very presence within Israel brought them victory in their battles. However, one day an exuberant King David had the ark brought to Jerusalem on a cart. When the oxen that were pulling the cart stumbled, and the ark was about to fall, Uzzah put out his hand to steady the ark...and God killed him. This was because David had not obeyed the instructions on *how* to transport the ark. The priests were supposed to carry it on poles. In his zeal without knowledge, David had it put on a cart thinking that would be acceptable to God—but his error had terrible consequences.

When it comes to evangelism, it seems that for the last hundred years we've had zeal without knowledge, and our evangelistic effort has been very shaky. But we must not try to steady the modern method to help it along. Instead, we should understand that we haven't done things according to God's pattern. There is a right way and a wrong way to present the gospel, and we're suffering the terrible consequences of not doing it God's way. So let's make sure we follow the pattern of

Holy Scripture. If the teachings of this study aren't biblical, they should be quickly discarded. However, if they are biblical, they should be instantly adopted.

View the Video **The Summary of Salvation**

Discussion

1. Why would a doctor take the time to explain to a patient the symptoms of a disease before he offers the cure?

2. What can we learn from the doctor analogy about sharing the gospel?

3. Explain the concept "Law to the proud, grace to the humble."

4. Can you think of biblical examples of "Law to the proud and grace to the humble"?

5. The Bible speaks of the Law being "good." How can the Law be used in a way that is not good?

6. According to Scripture, how should we share our faith with a person living a sexually immoral lifestyle?

7. How would you witness to a Jewish person? A Muslim?

8. How does the Law reveal to us our true state? Explain the "dust" analogy in your own words.

9. Why don't sinners naturally thirst for righteousness? What do they love instead?

Out of the Comfort Zone Activity

Before the next session, speak to three non-Christian friends or coworkers and say, "I'm taking a course at church and as homework I have to ask some friends if they've had a Christian or other spiritual background. Can you help me with this?" If they're open, ask them for details. Just listen and write down their answers. After they explain their upbringing, thank them for their help and carry on a friendly conversation as you normally would.

Don't feel pressured to share the gospel at this point. This exercise is simply for you to ask people this question, and listen to the answers. However, if you feel led to share your faith, follow God's leading.

Close in Prayer

Program 5: Practice What You Preach

Opening Activity

Briefly share the results of the previous session's "Out of the Comfort Zone" assignment. Were you fearful to do the activity? What sort of negative thoughts (if any) came to your mind? Was one person more open and friendly than the others? Was it a relaxed conversation? Would you say the door is open for you to speak to this person again about spiritual things?

Food for Thought

The Bible says that we wrestle not against flesh and blood, but against spiritual forces (Ephesians 6:12). This is a direct reference to demons (evil spirits) that can bombard our minds with negative and sinful thoughts. More than likely, at about this point in the course, you will be having thoughts of just giving up. In addition, other things in your life will start to seem more important and demand more of your time, leaving you with little or no time to complete these assignments and/or this evangelism course. This is normal when it comes to reaching out to the lost. Again, one of Satan's most powerful weapons is fear, which often comes in the form of discouragement. Think of the word "dis-courage." Satan wants to rid you of your *courage*. So make sure you have a sensitive ear to these subtle thoughts; know their source. This is why you've got to continually remember your Gethsemane experience—where you laid down your will and said, "God, I want to do Your will in my life. And Your will is that none perish." Determine to continue in this course despite the discouragement, so that you are fully equipped to do His will.

Discussion

1. Why does it take courage to make the transition from natural things to spiritual things? Do you (or would you) find it difficult to bring up the things of God with a stranger? Why—what do you fear?

2. Do you think that well-written gospel tracts can be a legitimate way of helping to make the transition into spiritual things? If so, do you use them? If not, why not? How do you bring up the topic of spiritual things?

3. Who do you know in your family, at school, or at work who isn't saved? Do you care about their salvation? What are you doing to reach them (in addition to praying)?

4. What is a good "inoffensive" question to ask a stranger, to discover his spiritual condition?

5. Explain the world's understanding of the word "good." Now explain God's definition of the word.

6. If you ask someone if he thinks he is a good person, and he says that he is, what can you say next so he sees himself in light of God's standards?

7. What two things should we be trusting in if we have biblically shared the gospel with an unsaved person?

Out of the Comfort Zone Activity

Think of the person you called the previous week who was the most open and friendly. Call the individual back before the next session and say, "Hi. It's me again. I hope you don't mind but I've been given another assignment for my study course. I really appreciate what you said last time. Can you help me again? This week's question is, 'Would you consider yourself to be a good person?' And if so, could you tell me why you think so?"

After the person explains why he thinks he is a good person, be sure to thank him and say, "I hope you don't mind me calling and asking you these questions. If it's an imposition, please let me know. "

If the person asks why you're asking these questions or what the study course is about, you can simply respond, "It's a course on encouraging people to talk with their friends about things that matter in life." Again, there is no pressure to share the gospel at this point, unless you feel led by God to do so.

Close in Prayer

Program 6: Idolatry—The Darling Sin of Humanity

Open in Prayer

Opening Activity

Briefly share the results of the previous session's "Out of the Comfort Zone" assignment. Did your friend say he was a good person? Why did he think so?

Food for Thought

Think deeply about what you are learning in this course. You are learning how to share your faith with others—how to bring the message of everlasting life to your hell-bound family member, friend, or coworker. All human beings have a fear of death, and in their heart of hearts, they're crying, "I don't want to die!" Some admit this; others are too proud to do so. But every one of us has a God-given will to live. Consider that God wants to use you to take the message of eternal life to a hopeless and dying humanity. Your task is infinitely more important than that of a skilled doctor who saves a patient from a terminal disease. His job is merely temporal; the person will die anyway. You have the privilege of being involved in that which is eternal. So consider these thoughts and commit yourself wholeheartedly to such an honorable and sobering task.

View the Video   **Idolatry—The Darling Sin of Humanity**

Discussion

1. Do you think *every* Christian has a moral responsibility to reach out to the lost, even those who don't feel they have a "gift" of evangelism? Discuss why or why not.

2. What is the First of the Ten Commandments? What does that mean to you personally as a Christian, in the area of sharing your faith?

3. What is the Second Commandment? Explain what this means, and how people today can form a god with whom they are more comfortable. Why do you think each of us naturally leans toward idolatry?

4. Were you an idolater before you came to faith in Jesus? Briefly explain your personal form of idolatry before becoming a Christian.

5. Think of someone you care about who is an idolater. What is his god like?

6. Discuss why idolatry is perhaps the deadliest of all sins.

7. Why is idolatry ("to me God is like...") unintelligent and foolish?

8. Why is "hell-fire preaching" unreasonable? How is biblical evangelism different from "hell-fire preaching"?

9. Explain why Felix "trembled" (Acts 24:25).

10. Is "fear" a legitimate motivator to cause a person to come to Christ—to flee from the wrath to come? (See Acts 17:30,31; 1 Thessalonians 1:10.) Discuss how fear can be positive.

11. Was "the fear of the Lord" a motivating factor in your conversion?

Out of the Comfort Zone Activity

Call your helpful friend (the same person you talked with last week) and explain that you do have another question for him. Say, "Last week you said that you were a good person. This week's question is a test to see if that's true. Would you be willing to give it a try? (Be sure to get permission.) We will simply go through a few of the Ten Commandments. Here we go: Have you ever told a lie? Have you ever stolen anything? Have you ever looked at someone with lust (which Jesus said is the same as committing adultery)? Etc. By now you should be very familiar with how to do this, having seen it done many times on the program. Don't listen to your fears; instead, think of the person's eternal welfare (we know you can do it). Go through as many of the Commandments as you can and end with, "It's certainly interesting to look at it from God's perspective, isn't it? Thanks for your honesty."

Again, there is no pressure to share the gospel with the person, unless you feel led to go further. If you sense that he is convicted by his sin, and you want to continue the conversation, follow the Lord's leading!

Close in Prayer

Program 7: The Beauty of a Broken Spirit—Atheism

Open in Prayer

Opening Activity

Briefly share the results of the previous session's "Out of the Comfort Zone" assignment.

Food for Thought

Most Christians feel intellectually intimidated when they witness to a professing atheist. This is because we have bought into the lie that atheism and intellectualism are synonymous. The exact opposite is true. The Bible tells us that those who profess to be atheists aren't thinking intelligently when it comes to God; they are fools (Psalm 14:1). It makes far more sense that a man denies the existence of the sun on a cloudless day than it does for him to deny the existence of God.

In today's program you will see a unique way to humble an atheist (or any proud person). Have someone in your study group ask the following five questions out loud. Do not call out any of the answers. This is important. Listen carefully, because the questions will not be repeated. *Write down* your responses:

1) What is the name of the raised print that deaf people use?

2) How many of each animal did Moses take into the ark?

3) Spell the word "shop." (Everyone in the group should answer this part *out loud* together, then write down the answer to the following question.) What do you do when you come to a green light?

4) Listen carefully. You are the driver of a train. There are thirty people on board. At the first stop ten people get on. At the

next stop, five people get off. Now for the question: What is the name of the train driver?

5) It is noon. You look at the clock. The big hand is on three, and the little hand is on five. What time is it?

The answers appear at the end of this lesson.

View the Video   The Beauty of a Broken Spirit—Atheism

Discussion

1. In light of the absurdity of the evolution of the soda can, why do you think so many people deny that there is an intelligent Creator?

2. Why do you think many Christians feel intimidated about sharing their faith with people who profess to be atheists?

3. Many claim that there is no proof for God's existence. Is that true?

4. Do you like the building/builder analogy? What other evidence can you use to prove the existence of God?

5. "There is no God" is an absolute statement. Do you think an atheist can make that statement (with integrity)? Why or why not?

6. How much knowledge do you think is possessed by the most brilliant person in the world? Is that enough to *know* that there is no God?

7. Why is there no such thing as an atheist?

8. After an atheist begins to backslide (change his mind about God), why is it important to swing from the area of the intellect to the conscience? Did you notice how the backsliding atheist in the video clip was feeling conviction of sin despite his atheistic statements?

9. How can a person find absolute proof of God's existence and the truth of Jesus' words? (See John 7:17; 14:21.)

Out of the Comfort Zone Activity

From the "Ice Breakers" sample pack included with this course, have each person in the group take a few tracts. Go over the suggestions on how to use each tract, then use these "ice breakers" with unbelievers before the next session.

If you just can't stand the thought of handing someone any piece of literature, simply start a conversation with a friend or stranger, bring up the things of God, and share your faith. A well-designed tract, however, helps by breaking the ice, opening up the conversation about God, and making the whole experience easier. We offer many unique tracts through our website at www.wayofthemaster.com.

Remember, the key is not to consider your own welfare but the eternal welfare of the unsaved person. The worst thing that could happen to you is that you will be rejected. The worst that could happen to the person to whom you are giving the tract is that he will spend eternity in hell. Ask God to give you compassion that will swallow your fears. Remember your Gethsemane experience, say, "I can do all things through Christ who strengthens me," then do it. Simply ask, "Did you get one of these?" Then run if you must...

Close in Prayer

Here are the answers to "Food for Thought":
1) *Deaf* people don't use Braille. 2) *Moses* didn't take any animals into the ark. 3) You *go* at a *green* light. 4) *You* are the driver of the train. 5) It is noon.

Program 8: WDJD?

Open in Prayer

Opening Activity

Briefly share the results of the previous session's "Out of the Comfort Zone" assignment.

Food for Thought

We're getting near the end of this course. How is your fear factor? Have you had discouraging thoughts? Any exhilarating moments of sharing your faith over the last few weeks? There is a positive side to the enemy's whisperings: fear can make you pray. A continual "You can't do this…" can deepen your trust in God. The negative of fear can then become the positive of prayer. So don't let fear stop you in your tracks. Instead, let it remind you to rely on God's strength, wisdom, and ability. It was fear that drove Jesus to His knees in the Garden of Gethsemane. Let fear bring you to your knees, then deny yourself, and unashamedly pick up the cross and follow Him who gave His life for this lost and dying world.

View the Video   WDJD?

Discussion

1. Do you feel inadequate or inferior when it comes to sharing your faith? Why?

2. What promises of God can help you in your inadequacies?

3. What is the first thing you must learn to do to get your feet wet? Why is this so difficult?

5. What is the first "steppingstone"? Could you ask someone this "steppingstone" question (after you have brought up the subject of spiritual things)?

6. What is the second steppingstone? Would you find this question difficult to ask?

7. What is the third steppingstone?

8. What is the fourth?

9. What should you remember about your tone of voice and your body language?

10. At what point in the conversation should you share the gospel?

Out of the Comfort Zone Activity

Determine to share your faith with someone. It can be the friend you called, a coworker, a family member, or a stranger. Again, the key is not to be concerned about yourself but to care about the unsaved person's fate. Even if your greatest fear came upon you and you were beaten up (or just humiliated), Jesus said to rejoice and be exceedingly glad because even the prophets before you were persecuted. Ask God to give you such love for people that you won't think of your own welfare, but only of theirs. Remember your Gethsemane experience, and stop listening to the lies of the devil. Say, "I can do all things through Christ who strengthens me." You may want to read the next section, "How to Witness," to review the principles you've learned in this course. Then do what you know you should. You will be glad you did.

Close in Prayer

How to Witness

The following information, much of which is taken from the program, will help to refresh your memory about what you learned. There is also additional information on how to deal with some of the common questions and objections to the Christian faith. You may even want to extend this study to discuss the content of this chapter.

Starting a Witnessing Encounter

To get your feet wet in witnessing, an easy first step is learning to be friendly and talk with people. This may seem obvious, but make a habit of talking to your family members and friends regularly. Then practice being friendly with people at the park, at the gas station, or at the grocery store. Perhaps you already have an outgoing and friendly personality—that's great! If you tend to be a shy, introverted person, try to open up a little and start talking with people. A simple "Hi, how are you?" isn't difficult. Or say, "Nice day, isn't it? My name is so and so..." With a bit of practice, anyone can learn to be friendly. Most people respond warmly to warmth.

To share our faith effectively, we must let people know that we are not "weirdos" or religious fanatics. We must show them that we care, and we start by being friendly. A good friend (who is admittedly quite shy) recently mentioned that he and a buddy went to the park on a Saturday afternoon, just to practice being friendly to strangers. They had a great time, and had so much fun that they couldn't wait to get out the following weekend to take the next step.

After you have gained a measure of confidence in speaking to strangers, you can swing to the subject of spiritual things.

It's not wise to walk up to people and immediately assault them with talk about Jesus. They'll most likely think you're strange. Instead, start in the natural realm (everyday things) and then swing to the spiritual realm. That's what Jesus did (see John chapter 4). He began talking to the woman at the well about natural things, then He swung to spiritual things. You may want to talk about sports or the weather, and then perhaps use something in the news to swing into the subject of spiritual things.

Alternatively, you can simply ask if the person knows of a good church in the area. Or you can use a gospel tract. It doesn't matter how you do it, as long as you do it. Start in the natural realm so the person doesn't think you're a religious nut, and then make the transition any way you want. That will lead you directly into the conversation about God.

WDJD: The Four Steppingstones

If you can remember four points, you can confidently lead *any* witnessing encounter. You will be in control of every conversation you have about your faith. Imagine—you will know exactly where you are in a conversation and you will know exactly where it is going. You don't have to study Greek; you don't have to understand archaeology; you just have to follow four "steppingstones" to reach your goal. You can say goodbye to your fears. These steppingstones can be easily remembered using the acronym WDJD.

There is no doubt that the first point is the most difficult to ask. Once you've brought up the subject of spiritual things, it becomes much easier. Here are the four steppingstones.

W: Would you consider yourself to be a good person?

You will be surprised to find that people are not offended by this question. If they say "No" (highly unlikely), ask them what they mean. Remember, you are asking people about their favorite subject—themselves. Most likely you'll find that they are kidding or that they've done something in their life that they feel badly about.

Otherwise, expect individuals to respond, "I'm a pretty good person" or "I'm a *really* good person." This reveals their pride and their self-righteousness. At this point you are ready to use the Law (the Ten Commandments) to humble them... the way Jesus did. Now move to the next steppingstone.

D: Do you think you have kept the Ten Commandments?

Some will say yes, others will say no. Regardless, you simply continue by saying, "Let's take a look at a few and see. Have you ever told a lie?" Some will admit to lying; others will say they have told only "white lies"; a few will claim they have never told even one lie. Gently press the issue: "Do you mean to say that you have never told anyone a lie to deceive them? Even once?" Usually they will say something like, "Maybe when I was a kid." Ask, "What does that make you?" They will hesitate to say, but get them to admit, "A liar."

People do not get angry with this approach; instead, they become sober. They may declare, "I don't believe in the Bible." Simply continue on your course. If they argue about the Bible, say, "I know you don't believe it. I am simply sharing with you what the Bible says. Okay? Let's keep going."

Continue going through the Commandments. You may want to ask about stealing next, then the Seventh Commandment, then the Third. Here is an example of how to go through each one:

#9　We covered "lying" above.

#8　"Have you ever stolen anything?" Many will claim that they haven't. "Have you ever taken anything that did not belong to you, regardless of its value... anything? Even when you were younger? Be honest before God." Some will try to trivialize theft by saying that they stole when they were a child. Ask, "What does that make you?" and press them to say, "A thief."

#7   "Have you ever committed adultery?" Again, most will say no. Add, "Jesus said, 'Whoever looks upon a woman to lust after her has committed adultery with her already in his heart.' Have you ever looked at someone with lust?"

#3   "Have you ever taken the Lord's name in vain?" Some will try to wiggle out of this, but just push a little: "You mean you have never casually used God's name to express anger?" Most will admit to this one. Then gently explain, "So instead of using a four-letter filth word to express disgust, you have taken the name of the One who gave you life and everything that is precious to you, and you have dragged it through the mud. People don't even use Saddam Hussein's name to curse, and you have used Almighty God's name? That is called 'blasphemy,' and God promises that He will not hold anyone blameless who takes His name in vain."

Note: You should be noticing something at this point. The individual will either grow quiet (be "shut up under the Law," Roman 3:20) or will be getting agitated. If the person seems to recognize his guilt, you may want to say at this point, "By your own admission, you're a lying thief, a blasphemer, and an adulterer at heart, and we've only looked at four of the Ten Commandments." If he is still trying to defend himself ("I'm not a bad person"), go through a few more Commandments.

#6   "Have you ever murdered anyone?" Obviously, most will say that they haven't. Point out, "Jesus said that if you merely call your brother a fool, you are in danger of judgment, and the Bible says if you've ever hated anyone, you are a murderer in God's eyes. God does not simply judge actions, He knows the intentions of the heart."

#1   "Have you always put God first in your life?" Most will admit that they haven't. "God says that He is supposed to be the primary love of our life. In fact, Jesus said that our love for God should be so great that our love for our parents, kids, friends, even our own lives should seem like hatred by comparison."

#2 "Have you ever made an idol, a god to suit yourself?" People will usually say that they haven't. "Have you pursued money more than God? Then you have made money an idol. Have you given work more attention than God? Then work is an idol. If you think, 'God is loving and wouldn't send me to hell,' you are correct; your god wouldn't send anyone to hell, because your god doesn't exist. He is a figment of your imagination. You've created a god in your own mind that you're more comfortable with, and that is called 'idolatry.' It's the oldest sin in the Book and God warns us that idolaters will not inherit the Kingdom of God."

#5 "Have you always honored your parents, treating them in a way that is pleasing to God?"

#10 "Have you ever coveted, or jealously desired something that did not belong to you? Covetousness reveals a lack of gratitude for what God has already given you."

#4 "Have you kept the Sabbath holy? God requires one day out of seven for you to rest and acknowledge Him, and you have failed to give Him what He has demanded. How many times you have neglected to bow your head before your meal and thank Him for the food He has provided? How many thousands of times do you think you've just greedily dug in without thanking your Provider?"

J—Judgment: If God judges you by the Ten Commandments on the Day of Judgment, will you be *innocent* or *guilty?*

If the individual has not yet begun to show signs of conviction, he will more than likely start now. Most people will sense where you are going with the conversation and say, "Innocent."

But they must understand and confess their guilt if they are ever to come to Jesus. The following will help them do that. Use this as a guide in directing the conversation and dealing with common responses. Again, this is not a script for what to say; feel free to use your own words.

Them: "I'm a pretty good person."

You: "You just told me that you broke God's Commandments. By your own admission, you're a lying thief, an adulterer at heart, a murderer, and blasphemer. Think about it. Will you be innocent or guilty?"

Them: "But I haven't done those things for a long time."

You: "Imagine saying that in a court of law. 'Judge, I know I am guilty but it has been years.' He won't ignore your crime. He will see that justice is served and will punish you no matter how much time has elapsed. The courts punish war criminals from decades ago, and God doesn't forget sin no matter how long ago a person did it. Do you think you will be innocent or guilty?"

Them: "But I have done more good than bad."

You: "Again, think of a court of law. If you have broken the law, you are guilty. It doesn't matter how many good deeds you've done when you are being tried for your crime. You have broken God's Law. Will you be innocent or guilty?"

Them: "But that's man's law. God is different."

You: "You're right. God can never be bribed. And His standards are much higher than a human judge's. He loves justice and has promised that He will punish not only murderers and rapists, but also liars, thieves, adulterers, and blasphemers. You are in big trouble, aren't you?"

Often, people become awakened (aware of their sin), but not alarmed. In other words, they understand they have broken God's Law, but it seems that they just don't care. Your goal is to see them alarmed, because they should be—they are in great danger. This line of reasoning can help:

> Let's imagine that a computer chip had been placed behind your ear, and it records everything that runs through your mind for a whole week: every secret thought, every deed, and every word that comes out of your mouth. Then all of your friends and family are called together and all of your thoughts are displayed on a big screen for them to see. How would that make you feel? Embarrassed? Ashamed? That is just what will happen on the day when God requires you to give an account for everything you've said and done for your whole life. All of your secret thoughts will be laid before Him. You are in big trouble.

It is wonderful to get a confession of guilt, but if the person simply won't be honest and admit his guilt, at some point you may have to help him. Say, "If you would just be honest, you know you will be guilty before God. Besides, that is what the Bible says and if you claim to be innocent, you are calling God a liar."

D—Destiny: Will you go to heaven or hell?

Gently ask, "Do you think you will go to heaven or hell?" People won't be offended because you are simply asking a question, rather than telling them where they're going. Some will say, "Hell," but most will say, "Heaven." If they think they are going to heaven, you can use this analogy:

> Consider this. You are standing in a court of law, guilty of a serious crime. There is a $50,000 fine. The judge says, "You are guilty. Anything to say before I pass sentence?" You answer, "Yes, judge. I'm sorry for what I have done. Please forgive me." Can a good judge let you go simply because you say that you are sorry, or that you won't do it again? Of course not. There is a $50,000 fine

that must be paid. However, if someone pays the fine for you, can the judge then let you go? Yes; once the fine has been paid, your debt to the law has been satisfied and the judge can set you free.

In the same way, each of us is guilty before God, and He will not let us go simply because we say that we are sorry or that we won't do it again. Of course, we should be sorry, and we shouldn't do it again. However, the fine for our crime must still be paid.

If the person responds by saying that this is man's justice, and that God's ways are different, agree with him. Say that God's justice is far harsher than man's justice, and that His standards are infinitely higher.

Do not be afraid to tell people that if they die in their sins, the Bible makes it clear that they will go to hell. Ask, "Does that concern you?"

If they say that it doesn't concern them, or if you sense they are not humbled and don't recognize their need of God's forgiveness, it's very helpful to describe what hell is like until they show signs of concern. According to the Bible, hell is a place of eternal, conscious torment, where "the worm dies not, and the fire is not quenched"; there is "weeping and gnashing of teeth," "everlasting punishment," "shame and everlasting contempt," and "eternal fire . . . the blackness of darkness for ever." Tell them that you don't want them to go to hell, and God doesn't want them to go to hell. Plead with them. If they do not seem concerned, it may be that they are just hiding it.

Don't feel pressured to give the Good News to a proud, self-righteous sinner (rebellious, cussing, arrogant) who is not willing to admit his guilt before God. Remember, Jesus didn't give the gospel to the rich, young ruler because he needed the Law to humble him first. You will have to watch and listen carefully because humility is not always obvious.

If the person admits that it does concern him, only at that point should you go to the gospel. If you are able to detect humility (the person is no longer justifying and defending himself), or his responses indicate that he has been humbled, you now have the glorious pleasure of sharing the Good News.

Sharing the Gospel

The Good News

Here's a good way to begin sharing the gospel: "God provided a way for you to be forgiven. The question is, how do you access this forgiveness?" Take the time to explain this thoroughly: "God loves you so much that He sent His only Son to suffer and die in your place, taking your punishment for you so that you could live. It is this simple: you broke the Law and Jesus paid your fine. Then Jesus rose from the dead and defeated death. If you will repent—turn away from sin—and place your trust in Jesus Christ as your Savior, God will forgive you and grant you everlasting life. He will change you from the inside out, and make you a new person in Christ."

This is the time to *magnify the love of God* to the sinner. Now you have the green light—go for it! Don't hold back: show the amazing length, width, depth, and height of God's love for the person as a sinner. This is when you pull out John 3:16. God offers complete forgiveness of sin and the gift of everlasting life *freely* to those who will surrender everything to Him through faith in Jesus Christ.

Ask the individual if he understands what you have told him. If he is willing to confess and turn from his sins and trust the Savior for his eternal salvation, have him pray and ask God to forgive him.

The Prayer

Should we pray the traditional sinner's prayer with someone who we think is willing to turn from sin and receive Christ? Perhaps this will shed some light on the subject: If someone you know committed adultery, would you lead him back to his wife and say, "Repeat after me: 'I am really sorry. I should not have slept with that woman'"? More than likely you wouldn't.

If someone says he wants to pray right then and there, encourage him to do so. You might like to say, "You can pray right now. Confess your sins and turn from them, and then tell God you are placing your trust in Jesus as the Lord and Savior of your life. Surrender your heart to Him. After you've prayed, I'll pray for you."

Then make sure the person has a Bible (get him one if necessary), and encourage him to read it daily and obey what he reads. Also, encourage him to get into a Bible-believing, Christ-centered church.

If the person doesn't ask you to pray with him, let him go on his way, but encourage him to think deeply about your conversation and to get his heart right with the Lord as soon as possible. You can then leave him in the hands of a faithful God, who will continue to speak to him through His Holy Spirit and bring him to genuine repentance in His time.

For a thorough treatment on why we should be very careful about hastily leading someone in a prayer for salvation, visit our website at www.wayofthemaster.com and check out "How to Botch an Altar Call" (under Free Tools / Extras).

Inoculated "Almost-Christians"

If you are dealing with an inoculated churchgoer who knows a few Bible verses (such as John 3:16), you probably have the toughest encounter of all. The person may answer all the questions correctly, but you know he doesn't live like a Christian should. Here are some questions that might reveal his level of understanding:

1. "Are you born again?" If he says he isn't, remind him that Jesus said a man must be born again to enter the Kingdom of God (John 3:5).

2. "When was the last time you read your Bible?" If he says it's been a long time, express your concern by asking, "What would you think if you sent love letters to your wife and she never took the time to read them? You would start to sus-

pect that maybe she isn't very interested in you. God sent you sixty-six letters and you rarely read them. What should He conclude about your love for Him?"

Encourage the person to examine himself to see if he is in the faith (2 Corinthians 13:5). If there are no signs that he has been born again, if there is no fruit in his life to indicate that he is a child of God, ask, "Do you consider yourself to be a good person?" If he says yes, something is radically wrong, and you should take him through the Law.

The Place of Apologetics

While apologetics (defense of the faith) play an important part in evangelism, it's vital to realize that they have a limited function in reaching the lost. If we confine our witness to arguing about the existence of God, the inspiration of Scripture, the age of the earth, etc., we are like a man who goes fishing with bait, but no hook. While he may attract the fish, they will end up fat and happy...and they will get away. The function of bait is to attract the fish and disguise the hook. When the fish come around, the fisherman pulls the hook into the jaw, and catches his fish. Apologetics are the bait, and the hook is God's Law. It is the Law that appeals to a man's conscience and brings the knowledge of sin.

Hell-fire Preaching

It's important to realize that when we talk about the Law and the reality of hell and Judgment Day, we aren't referring to "hell-fire preaching." Hell-fire preaching will produce fear-filled converts. Using God's Law will produce tear-filled converts. Those who hear only the message of hell, without the Law to make it reasonable, come to Christ because they want to escape the fires of hell. But in their heart, they think God is harsh and unjust, because the Law hasn't been used to show them the exceedingly sinful nature of sin. They don't see that they *deserve* eternal damnation, that hell is their just dessert.

They don't understand mercy or grace, and therefore lack gratitude to God for the cross—and gratitude is the prime motivation for evangelism. There will be no zeal in the heart of a false convert to evangelize.

However, those who hear and understand the Law come to Christ knowing they have sinned against heaven. They know that God's eye is in every place beholding the evil and the good, and that God has seen darkness as though it were pure light. He's seen their thought-life. If on the Day of Judgment God in His holiness exposed all the secret sins of their hearts, if He revealed all the evidence of their guilt, He could pick them up as an unclean thing and cast them into hell *and do that which is just and right*. But instead of giving them justice, He has given them mercy. He's demonstrated His love toward them in that while they are yet sinners, Christ died for them. They fall on their knees before that bloodstained cross and say, "Oh, God, if You did that for me, I'll do anything for You. I delight to do Your will, oh, my God. Your law is written on my heart."

Helpful Analogies to Use in Witnessing

If the person to whom you are witnessing seems to be having trouble understanding a spiritual truth, you may find these analogies helpful. (See *The Evidence Bible* for these and many others.)

You Don't Just "Believe" in a Parachute

A churchgoer may need help understanding the difference between just "believing in Jesus" and being "born again." Say, "If you and I were on an airplane and we knew we were about to crash, and I had my parachute on and you didn't, what is the most loving thing I could do for you? It would be to tell you to put on your parachute! If you told me you already believed in the parachute under your seat, but you didn't put it on, I'd plead with you to strap it on right away—because I know what will happen to you if you jump without the parachute. Simply believing in a parachute will not help you; you must put it on for it to do you any good. That's what the Bible says you must do with Jesus. It's not enough to simply 'believe' in Jesus (even the demons 'believe'); you must 'put on the Lord Jesus Christ' in order to be saved. You do that by repenting and placing your trust in Jesus as Lord and Savior. It's called being born again."

The Good Judge

A person may say that, although he's sinned against God, he will go to heaven anyway. This is usually because he thinks that God is "good," and that He will therefore overlook sin in his case. Point out that if a judge in a criminal case has a guilty murderer standing before him, the judge, if he is a good man, can't just let him go. He must ensure that the guilty man is punished. Say, "If the judge just let him go, he'd be a corrupt judge and should himself be brought to justice. If he's a good judge, he will do everything in his power to see that justice is served. Likewise, if God is good, He must (by nature) punish murderers, rapists, thieves, liars, adulterers, fornicators, and those who have lived in rebellion to His Law and to the inner light that God has given to every man."

But God is also rich in mercy, not wanting anyone to perish. He demonstrated His love for us on the cross. Tell the person, "We broke God's Law and Jesus paid our fine. If you will repent and trust in the Savior, God will forgive your sins and dismiss your case."

The Value of a Soul

If the person you are witnessing to doesn't seem to understand the seriousness of immediately getting right before God, try this: "Would you sell one of your eyes for a million dollars? What about both of them for ten million? Of course you wouldn't—no one in his right mind would—because your eyes are precious to you. If you think about it, your eyes are merely the windows of your soul (your life). Your life 'looks' out of your eyes. If your eyes are precious to you, how much more should you value your life? Jesus said, 'If your eye causes you to sin, pluck it out. It is better for you to enter the Kingdom of God with one eye, rather than having two eyes, to be cast into hell fire.' Jesus also said, 'What will it profit a man if he gains the whole world, and loses his own soul?' There is nothing more important than your own soul and where you will spend eternity."

Right in His Own Eyes

Many people don't think about the consequences of their actions and don't realize that they themselves are responsible. Consider the way dogs cross the road. A dog will wander onto a freeway oblivious to the danger. His tail wags as he steps between cars without a second thought. Cars swerve. Tires squeal. The noise is deafening as vehicles smash into each other. The sleepy dog stops wagging his tail for a moment and looks at the pile of smoldering, broken cars on the freeway. His expression betrays his thoughts. His bone-burying brain doesn't realize for one moment that he is responsible for the disaster.

When man wanders onto the freeway of sin, his tail wags with delight. He thinks that this is what he was made for. His thoughts of any repercussions for his actions are shallow. His mind wanders into lust, then predictably he wanders onto the path of adultery. Suddenly a disaster sits before him. His marriage is shattered, his name is slurred, his children are twisted and scarred. But like the dumb dog, he doesn't realize for one moment that he is solely responsible for his sin. What he has done is right in his own eyes. This is why the perfect Law of God needs to be arrayed before his darkened eyes—to show him that his way is not right in the eyes of a perfect God.

Responses to Common Arguments

Being prepared with ready responses to some of the common arguments will help you feel more confident as you witness.

"I don't believe in hell."

If an individual claims not to believe in hell, gently respond, "That doesn't matter. You still have to face God on Judgment Day *whether you believe in it or not.* If I step onto the freeway when a massive truck is heading for me and I say, 'I don't believe in trucks,' my lack of belief isn't going to change reality."

"I just hope God is forgiving."

Someone who acknowledges his sins but is relying on God's forgiveness could be referred to as "awakened, but not alarmed." Explain that God is forgiving—but only to those who repent of their sins. Ask him, "If you died right now, where would you go?" If he says, "Hell," ask if that concerns him. If it does concern him, ask, "What are you going to do?" Then tell him that God commands him to repent and trust the Savior. If it doesn't concern him, speak of the value of his life, the threat of eternal damnation, and the biblical description of hell. Caution him that he doesn't have the promise of tomorrow, and plead with him to come to his senses.

"You are trying to make me feel guilty by quoting the Ten Commandments."

Ask the person which one of the Ten Commandments makes him feel guilty. Simply state, "The Bible says, 'You shall not steal.' If you feel guilty when you hear that, why do you think that is? Could it be because you are guilty?" God gave us our conscience so we would know when we break His Law; the guilt we feel when we do something wrong tells us that we need to repent.

Important Points to Remember in Witnessing

Communication consists of more than our words. When it comes to sharing our faith, there are certain aspects that we often overlook. The following are points to keep in mind.

Tone of Voice

It is imperative that we ask God for the right spirit, tone, and attitude in a witnessing encounter. We don't want to come across like a "know-it-all," or as arrogant. Our attitude should be humble compassion mixed with a deep concern. Be resolute, but gentle. Don't be smug with your arguments. We're called to speak with gentleness and respect, like compassionate doctors with a cure. We should never become angry, or even raise our voice. We have the freedom to speak very boldly, if the hearer senses that we are coming from a place of love and concern.

Gestures

Don't point your finger at someone in a judgmental way. Be careful even of your body language. Don't stand above people if you can help it; sit down beside them. Don't have a smug grin on your face as though you are winning an argument, or fold your arms as though you are scolding a child. Remember, above all, that you are only a fellow sinner saved by God's grace, pleading with others to come to the Savior.

Your Testimony and the Law

If you choose to give your testimony when witnessing, remember to weave in the Law. Here's how *not* to testify: "Before I knew Jesus, I was sad and unfulfilled. I tried everything but it just didn't make me happy. Then I gave my heart to Jesus and I have been so happy ever since." Remember, that will introduce a false motive. Instead, say something like this:

> Years ago I lived for myself. Then I looked at the Ten Commandments and I realized that I had broken God's Law. I began to understand that He saw me as a liar, and that all liars will have their place in the Lake of Fire. I realized that I had used His holy name as a filth word, and that He doesn't hold people guiltless who take His name in vain. [Go through all Ten Commandments if you are able to.] That is when I realized I was going to be in big trouble on Judgment Day, and that I deserved to go to hell. I certainly didn't want to go to hell—that's a place I never want to experience. Then I heard that Jesus did something truly amazing: two thousand years ago, He was brutally whipped and beaten, and nailed to a cross. He willingly shed His blood in my place so that I could be forgiven. I broke the Law and Jesus paid my fine—He took my punishment for me.

> When I heard that, I dropped to my knees, confessed my sins to God, and gave my life to Jesus Christ. Ever since then, I have been reading the Bible because I want to know more and more about the One who loves me so much that He died for me. Now I know that I have eternal life, and will be found "not guilty" on the Day of Judgment—not because I'm a good person, but simply because of God's mercy.

This testimony is only an example, showing how to properly present the issues. Obviously, you need to tailor your story to reflect your personal experience. It is important to remember the principal of law before grace, and to use the Moral Law to bring the knowledge of sin before sharing the gospel.

Loving Our Neighbors

The greatest way to love our neighbors is to share the gospel with them. But neighbors are like family—we don't want to offend them unnecessarily, because we have to live with them. We need to be rich in good works toward all men, but especially our neighbors. The Bible reveals that good works are a legitimate means of evangelism. Jesus said, "Let your light so shine before men, that they may see your good works, and glorify your Father who is in heaven" (Matthew 5:16). It is God's will that "with well doing you may put to silence the ignorance of foolish men" (1 Peter 2:15). Sinners may disagree with what you believe, but seeing your good works makes them think, "I don't believe what he believes, but he sure does. He certainly is sincere in his faith."

A friendly wave, a gift for no reason, fresh-baked goods, etc., can pave the way for evangelism. Offer to mow your neighbors' lawn or help do some painting. Volunteer to pick up their mail and newspapers while they're on vacation. Compliment them on their landscaping and ask for gardening tips. Invite them over for a barbecue or dessert. Pray for an opportunity to share the gospel, and be prepared for it when it comes.

Practice

As you've watched the programs, you may have thought that you could never remember all the information. You don't have to. Just remember the WDJD steppingstones and practice them. Find a friend and role play. You had to practice almost everything else in life—walking, writing, reading, riding a bike, driving a car. Evangelism is no different. Once you have the four steppingstones memorized and begin putting them into practice, you will start an incredible evangelistic adventure. You will be amazed that the responses of those you speak to will be very predictable. In no time at all, sharing your faith will become second nature to you. What's more, God will be with you every step of the way.

Helpful Verses to Use When Witnessing

Exodus 20:1–17 (the Ten Commandments)

Psalm 51 (as an example of a prayer of repentance)

Isaiah 53:5,6

Ezekiel 18:4

Matthew 5:27,28

Matthew 12:36

Luke 13:3

Luke 16:15

John 3:16

John 3:18

John 3:36

John 14:21

Acts 4:12

Acts 17:30,31

Romans 2:5,6

1 Corinthians 6:9,10

Colossians 1:20–22

1 John 1:9,10

Other Resources

As the title of this study implies, *The Foundation Course* is merely the first step in learning how to share your faith. Although these foundational lessons cover the basics, we strongly encourage you to gain further education through a collection of wonderful illustrations, witnessing tips, quotes, etc., available in *The Evidence Bible* (Bridge-Logos Publishers). You can order a copy by phone at 877-486-8688, through your local Christian bookstore, or through our ministry website at www.wayofthemaster.com.

We also invite you to sign up for our monthly e-newsletter, containing ministry updates, candid thoughts and articles by Kirk Cameron and Ray Comfort, notices of new "ice breaker" tracts, special offers, etc. We want to be your witnessing resource center and a continual source of encouragement, inspiration, and blessing to you.

If you need more study guides, they are available at a special bulk price. For details, call 877-496-8688 or visit www.wayofthemaster.com.

The Evidence Bible

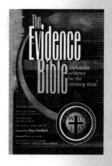

"*The Evidence Bible* is specially designed to reinforce the faith of our times by offering hard evidence and scientific proof for the thinking mind."
—Dr. D. James Kennedy

The Evidence Bible, based on more than two decades of research, has been commended by Josh McDowell, Franklin Graham, Dr. Woodrow Kroll, and many other Christian leaders.

- Learn how to show the absurdity of evolution.

- See from Scripture how to prove God's existence without the use of faith.

- Discover how to prove the authenticity of the Bible through prophecy.

- See how the Bible is full of eye-opening scientific and medical facts.

- Read fascinating quotes from Darwin, Einstein, Newton, and other well-known scientists.

- Learn how to share your faith with your family, neighbors, and coworkers, as well as Muslims, Mormons, Jehovah's Witnesses, etc.

- Glean evangelistic wisdom from Charles Spurgeon, John Wesley, George Whitefield, D. L. Moody, John MacArthur, and many others.

- Discover answers to 100 common objections to Christianity.

Find out how to answer questions such as: Where did Cain get his wife? Why is there suffering? Why are there "contradictions" in the Bible? . . . and much more!